ADVENTURES OF LOLLIPOP NUMBER 3

Lollipop: in and Out of this World!

JENNIFER CUTHBERT

PEPPERMINT PUBLISHING

Library and Archives Canada Cataloguing in Publication

Cuthbert, Jennifer, 1984-
Lollipop : in and out of this world! : adventures of Lollipop 3 / Jennifer Cuthbert.

ISBN 0-9732053-2-6

1. Voyages and travels—Comic books, strips, etc.
I. Title.

PN6733.C88L63 2005   j741.5'971   C2005-906414-5

Printed in Canada

1 2 3 4 5 6

CONTENTS

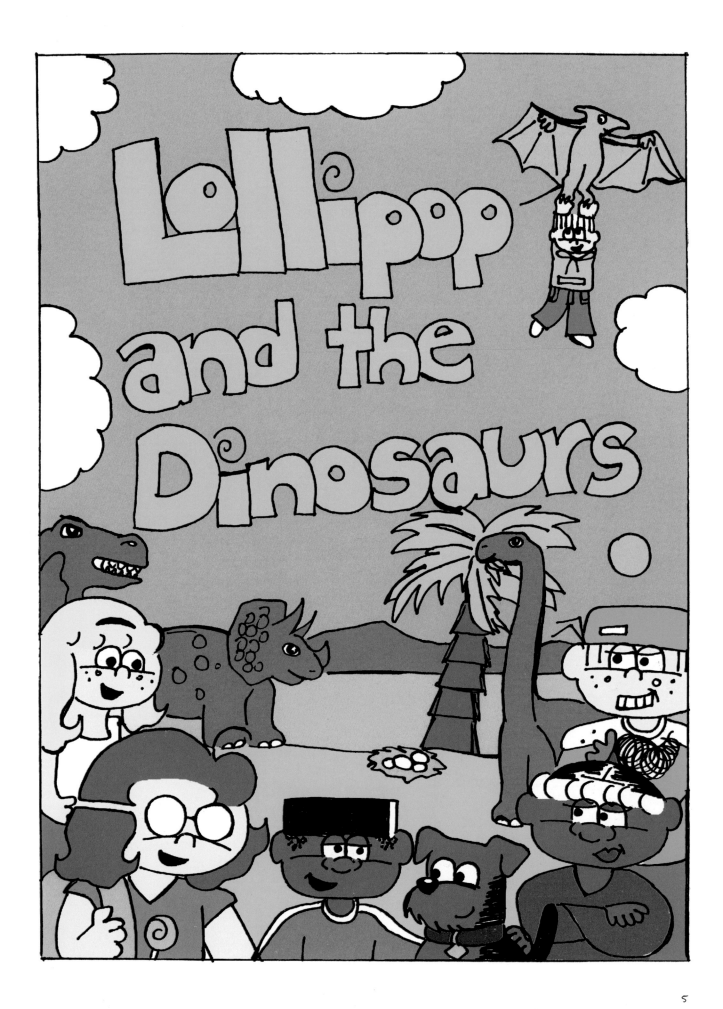

43

THE ADVENTURES OF LOLLIPOP

Join the Lollipop gang as they sample sushi and sumo wrestling in Japan, battle a wicked wizard in medieval times, meet a movie star in the land down under, and receive the royal treatment in ancient Egypt.

LOLLIPOP'S CANADA: COAST TO COAST!

Join Lollipop and her friends as they whale watch off the west coast, get into hot water in Banff and experience pioneer life on the Prairies. They venture to the top of Toronto, to the bottom of Niagara Falls and chill out at the Quebec Winter Carnival. The gang also experiences igloos, inukshucks and the Northern Lights in Nunavut and learn to love lobster on the east coast.

ABOUT THE AUTHOR

Jennifer Cuthbert is an undergraduate History student at York University in Toronto. Jennifer has been drawing and writing stories about Lollipop and her friends since the age of nine. She has published *The Adventures of Lollipop* and *Lollipop's Canada: Coast to Coast!* and frequently visits schools to share Lollipop stories. Jennifer lives in Brampton, Ontario with her parents, brother and dog, Fraser.